THE SMALLEST ANGEL

A Christmas Play with Music for Infants and Young Juniors
Words and Music by PATRICIA LEE

Note to Producer:
Writers and Publishers receive royalties through performances of their
works as well as the sale of sheet music. It would be greatly appreciated
therefore if application for a licence to perform this work could be made
in writing to International Music Publications, Southend Road, Woodford
Green, Essex, IG8 8HN. Please state the title of the work and the proposed
dates of performance.

Edited by STEPHEN CLARK
First Published 1988
© International Music Publications

Exclusive Distributors
International Music Publications
Southend Road, Woodford Green,
Essex IG8 8HN, England.

215-2-513

NOTES ON PERFORMANCE

The Smallest Angel will adapt easily to many different styles of presentation and may be performed successfully by large or small forces. The structure enables scenes 2-8 to be performed in any order. Teachers working with small numbers need not include every country.

Costumes may be as simple or elaborate as desired. Scenery is not necessary but the following will be useful:

Totem Pole (cardboard boxes), Palm tree (broom handle with stiff paper leaves), paper flowers, garlands, fans, cardboard skis, paper lanterns.

Most of these can be made by the children.

Percussion parts may be added using the instruments most characteristic to each country. The following are suggestions only:

North America	- Drum
Hawaii	- Xylophone, Glockenspiel *(glissandi)*
Spain	- Maracas, Tambourine, woodblock/castenets
Scotland	- Side Drum
Switzerland	- Bells
China	- Xylophone, Cymbals

The Smallest Angel is ideal as a basis for topic web/project work, based on the culture and life styles of each country. Working towards a performance gives additional opportunities for calculating seating, designing posters and printing tickets. The songs illustrate the popular musical idioms of each country and may be used out of context at any time of the year.

THE SMALLEST ANGEL

A Christmas Play with Music for Infants and Young Juniors
Words and Music by PATRICIA LEE

CONTENTS

Cast

THE SMALLEST ANGEL
ANGELS 1-6

RED INDIANS 1-4
HAWAIIANS 1-2
SPANIARDS 1-3
SCOTS 1-2
SWISS 1-4
CHINESE 1-2

MARY
JOSEPH
3 SHEPHERDS } mime only
3 WISE MEN

NARRATORS 1-2

CHORUS *of* RED INDIANS, HAWAIIANS, SPANIARDS,
SCOTS, SWISS *and* CHINESE *(any number).*

THE SMALLEST ANGEL

Words and Music by PATRICIA LEE

INTRODUCTORY MUSIC

5

HAVE YOU EVER WONDERED?

Scene 1: Heaven. The six ANGELS and THE SMALLEST
ANGEL take up their positions on stage.

ALL:
1. Have you ev - er wondered, don't you
2. But there is a sec - ret we would
(3.) an - gels up in hea - ven were sur-

think it's strange— That when God sent his on - ly son He did - n't ar-range ——— For
like to share.— We just can't keep it to our-selves, it would - n't seem fair. ——— We're
prised to hear —— The voice of God ring out to them so loud and so clear. ——— "I

some-thing more splen—did, fit for a king,—— A lux -ury cra-dle,— a
go - ing to tell — you, we're go-ing to show—— A part of the sto — ry
know you are bu — sy,—there's plen-ty to do,—— But I have a job — of

ANGEL 1:   We'd better leave right away.

The six ANGELS *turn to go.*

SMALLEST ANGEL: Hey! Wait for me.

ANGEL 2:   But you can't come.

SMALLEST ANGEL: Why not?

ANGEL 3:   You're much too small.

ANGEL 4:   And this job is very *important.*

ANGEL 5:   You can stay and look after everything
                            until we get back.

ANGEL 6:   We won't be long.

Exit ANGELS. THE SMALLEST ANGEL *follows
them, waving but looking unhappy.*

THE INDIAN CAMP

Scene 2: North America.
RED INDIANS take up their positions on stage.
ANGEL 1 approaches.

ANGEL 1
(to audience): This looks like a good place to start.
ANGEL 1 reaches the RED INDIANS *camp.*

ANGEL 1
(to INDIANS*):* Greetings.

INDIANS *(raising hand*
in traditional salute): How!

ANGEL 1: May I rest here?

INDIAN 1: You are welcome. My brothers and sisters will give
you food and drink.

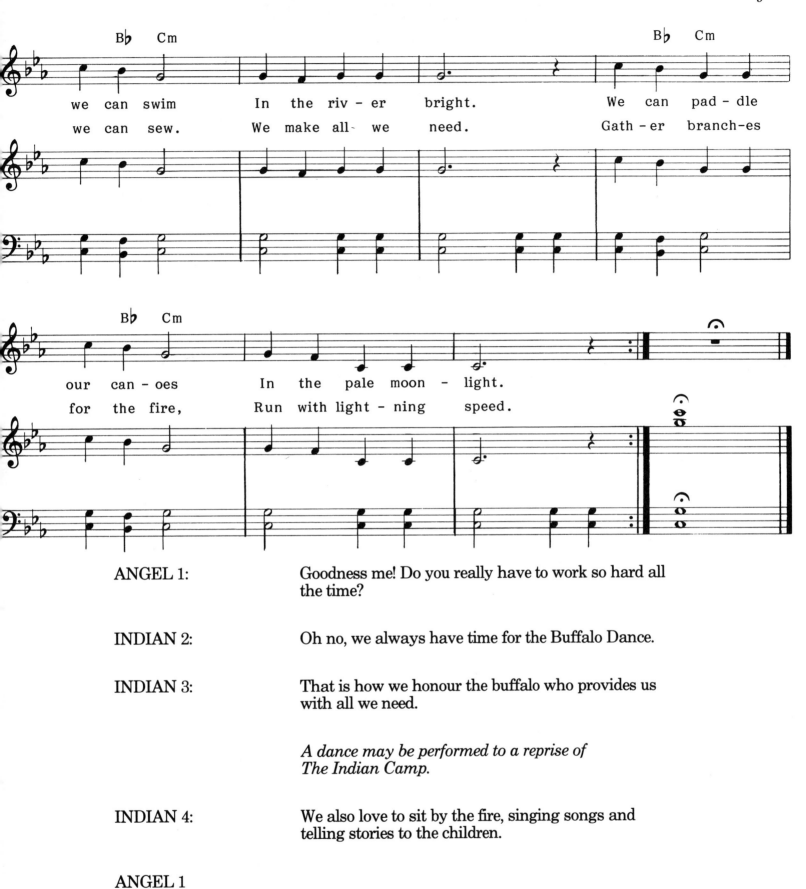

we can swim   In the riv-er   bright.   We can pad-dle
we can sew.   We make all we   need.   Gath-er branch-es

our can-oes   In the pale moon-light.
for the fire,   Run with light-ning speed.

ANGEL 1:   Goodness me! Do you really have to work so hard all
                the time?

INDIAN 2:   Oh no, we always have time for the Buffalo Dance.

INDIAN 3:   That is how we honour the buffalo who provides us
                with all we need.

                A dance may be performed to a reprise of
                The Indian Camp.

INDIAN 4:   We also love to sit by the fire, singing songs and
                telling stories to the children.

ANGEL 1
        (to audience):   I think I've found the perfect place for God's Son to
                            be born.
        (to INDIANS):   I am well rested now and I must be on my way.
                            Thank you for everything. Goodbye.

INDIANS: Farewell.

                Exit ANGEL 1, *followed by the* RED INDIANS.

HAWAIIAN ISLAND

Scene 3: Hawaii.

HAWAIIANS take up their positions on stage.
ANGEL 2 approaches.

ANGEL 2 *(to audience)*: What a lovely place. I'm sure no one else will find somewhere as special as this.

ANGEL 2 reaches Hawaii.

HAWAIIANS: Aloha!

Girls place garlands on the boys and ANGEL 2.

HAWAIIAN 1
(to ANGEL 2): We have just picked some pineapples. Would you like a piece?

HAWAIIAN 2: They're very juicy and sweet.

ANGEL 2: Yes please.

HAWAIIANS:
1. Blue blue sky and gold-en sand. Feel the gen-tle breeze that blows a-cross our land. High a-bove
2. Wa-ter clear where fish-es swim. And the shin-ing sun is warm up-on our skin. Ma-ny fruits

ANGEL 2 *(to audience)*: I think I'll go straight home. I can't imagine anywhere more perfect.

(to HAWAIIANS*)*: Goodbye.

HAWAIIANS *blow kisses and wave.*

Exit ANGEL 2, *followed by the* HAWAIIANS.

Scene 4: Heaven

Enter THE SMALLEST ANGEL. THE SMALLEST ANGEL *is seen waiting for the* ANGELS *to return.*

SMALLEST ANGEL: It's just not fair! Why should I have to stay here? I'm tired of being told I'm too small and I'm not waiting any longer. I will go and find the best place on the earth.

Exit THE SMALLEST ANGEL.

Scene 5: Spain

SPANIARDS *take up their positions, dancing and playing guitars.*
ANGEL 3 *approaches.*

ANGEL 3 *(to audience)*: These people seem to be enjoying themselves.
(to SPANIARDS*)*: Are you having a party?

SPANIARD 1: Yes, we are celebrating the end of the grape harvest.

SPANIARD 2: The grapes will be turned into wine.

SPANIARD 3: The best wine in the whole world.

LIFE IN SPAIN

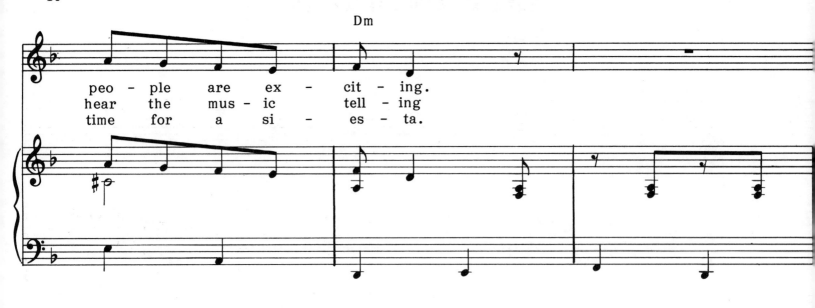

peo — ple   are   ex —   cit — ing.
hear   the   mus — ic   tell — ing
time   for   a   si —   es — ta.

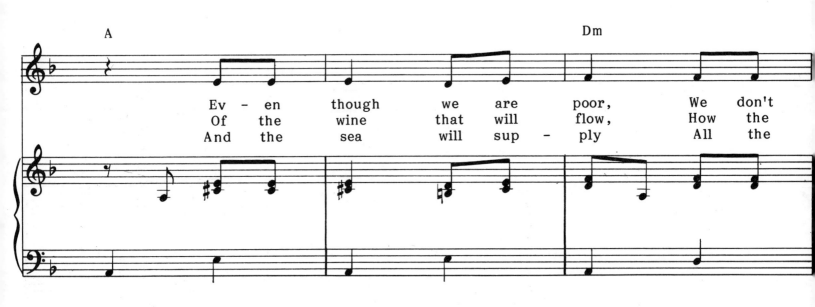

Ev — en   though   we   are   poor,   We   don't
Of   the   wine   that   will   flow,   How   the
And   the   sea   will   sup — ply   All   the

ask   for   much   more   Than   to   live   here   in
or — ang — es   grow   And   our   hearts   full   of
fish   we   can   fry   So   we   sing,   dance   and

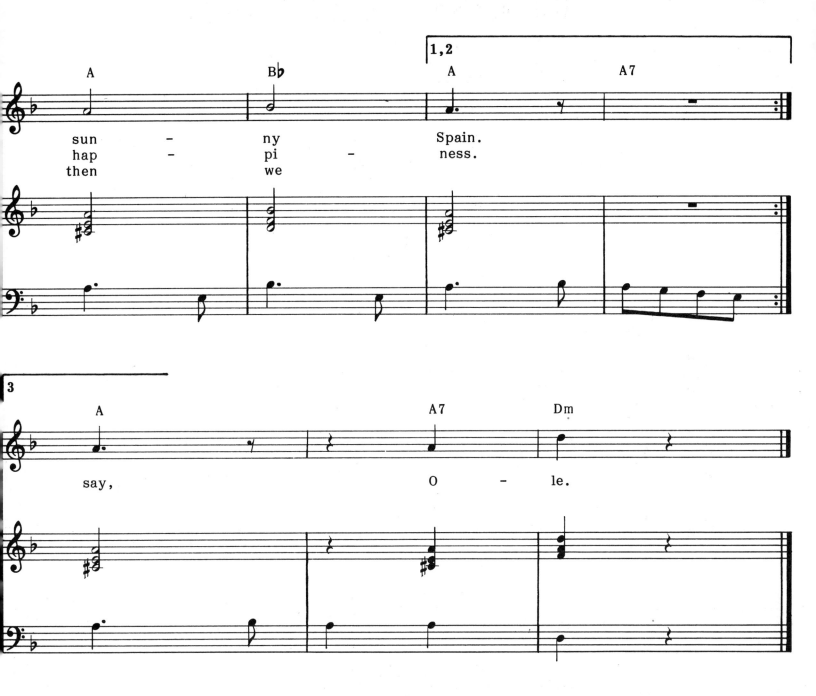

ANGEL 3:   I wish I could stay for the Fiesta but it's a long way
             back to Heaven. Goodbye.

SPANIARDS: Adios.
             Exit ANGEL 3, *followed by the* SPANIARDS.

IN BONNY SCOTLAND

Scene 6: Scotland

SCOTS *take up their positions.*
ANGEL 4 *approaches.*

ANGEL 4 *(to audience)*: Oh dear, it's raining. I wonder if I can find shelter here?

SCOT 1: Come in out of the rain.

SCOT 2: You'll catch a cold.

Brightly ♩ = 96

SCOTS:
1. Here in bon - ny Scot - land where the grass grows green, On the
2. Here in bon - ny Scot - land where the bag - pipes play, You can

high - lands and the low - lands And the bits found in be - tween. There's no
have a bowl of por - ridge Al - most an - y time of day. There's a

ANGEL 4:   I think it's stopped raining now. I'd better go home and find some dry clothes. Goodbye.

SCOTS: Cheerio.

Exit ANGEL 4, *followed by the* SCOTS.

THE SWISS ALPS

Scene 7: Switzerland.

SWISS *take up their positions.*
ANGEL 5 *approaches.*

ANGEL 5 *(to audience)*:   I bet God's Son would have fun in all this snow.

SWISS 1:   We're getting ready to go skiing.

SWISS 2:   Would you like to come with us?

ANGEL 5:   I'd better not but can you tell me more about your country.

SWISS 3:   Of course; come and warm yourself by the fire.

SWISS: 1. Here where the mountain goats wan-der free. This is the on-ly place for me.
2. When all the ground is cov-ered in snow, I have a cha-let where I go.

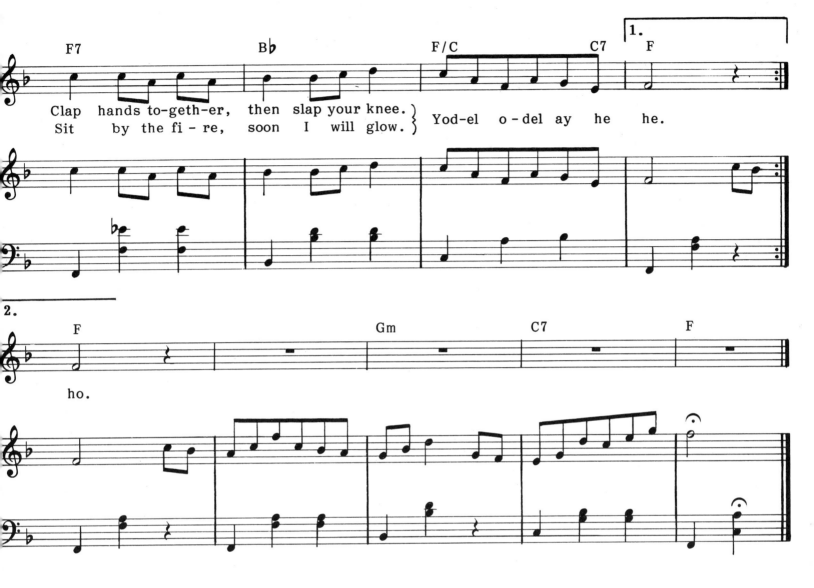

Clap hands to-geth-er, then slap your knee. } Yod-el o-del ay he he.
Sit by the fi - re, soon I will glow. }

ho.

ANGEL 5 *(to* SWISS*)*:   Thank you. Next time I visit I'll try those skis.

SWISS 4 *offers skis to* ANGEL 5.

SWISS 4:   You can take these with you.

ANGEL 5:   Thank you. Goodbye.

SWISS *(all)*:   Goodbye.

Exit ANGEL 5 *followed by the* SWISS.

CHINESE SPRINGTIME

Scene 8: China

CHINESE *take up their positions.*
ANGEL 6 *approaches.*

ANGEL 6 *(to audience):*   What a lovely garden! How peaceful and colourful it is.

CHINESE 1:   Can I help you?

ANGEL 6:   I was looking for somewhere special but I think I've found it.

CHINESE 2:   Let me show you around.

CHINESE: 1. Where in spring-time— can you see Cher-ry blos-som— on the trees?
3. Col-oured lan-terns in a row Cheer the night with a ro-sy glow.

Hear the weep-ing will-ow sigh As the stream goes rush-ing by.
Such sweet mus-ic fills the air; These are plea-sures we—can share.

TO ⊕ CODA

2. Lit-tle fat silk worms— feed all day, Be-fore they hide them— selves a-way.

When they've grown some wings in-stead, We will weave their silk— en thread.

ANGEL 6 and CHINESE *bow to each other.*

Exit ANGEL 6 *and* CHINESE.

Scene 9: Heaven.

The six ANGELS *have returned. They take up their positions on stage.*

NARRATOR 1:   When the angels returned to Heaven they told God of the places they had seen.

ANGELS *speak to audience.*

ANGEL 1:   I found somewhere with mountains and rivers.

ANGEL 2:   I found somewhere warm and beautiful.

ANGEL 3:   I went to a place where people dance and sing.

ANGEL 4:   It was raining where I went but the people were so friendly.

ANGEL 5:   Nowhere could be more fun than the snowy mountains.

ANGEL 6:   But nowhere could be more peaceful than a garden with cherry blossom.

NARRATOR 2:   God listened to them all and said, "The places you have found are very beautiful. But I want the birth of my Son to bring hope to those who are hungry, those who are sick and those who have nothing. You must search again."

NARRATOR 1:   But at that moment the smallest angel returned.

Enter THE SMALLEST ANGEL.

SMALLEST ANGEL: Oh please don't be angry. I wanted to help but I was so tired when I reached the earth, I fell asleep in a stable.

ANGELS 1-6:   A stable? *(surprised)*

NARRATOR 1:   God smiled and said, "If it's good enough for my smallest angel, it must be good enough for my Son."

NARRATOR 2:   So Jesus was born in a stable.

The ANGELS *and* THE SMALLEST ANGEL *move back.*

HAPPY BIRTHDAY JESUS

Scene 10: A Stable In Bethlehem.

MARY *and* JOSEPH *(with the baby Jesus) take
their positions in front of the* ANGELS.
The song HAPPY BIRTHDAY JESUS *is sung.*
SHEPHERDS *arrive during verse 1 to give a lamb.*
WISE MEN *arrive during verse 2 and present their
gifts.*

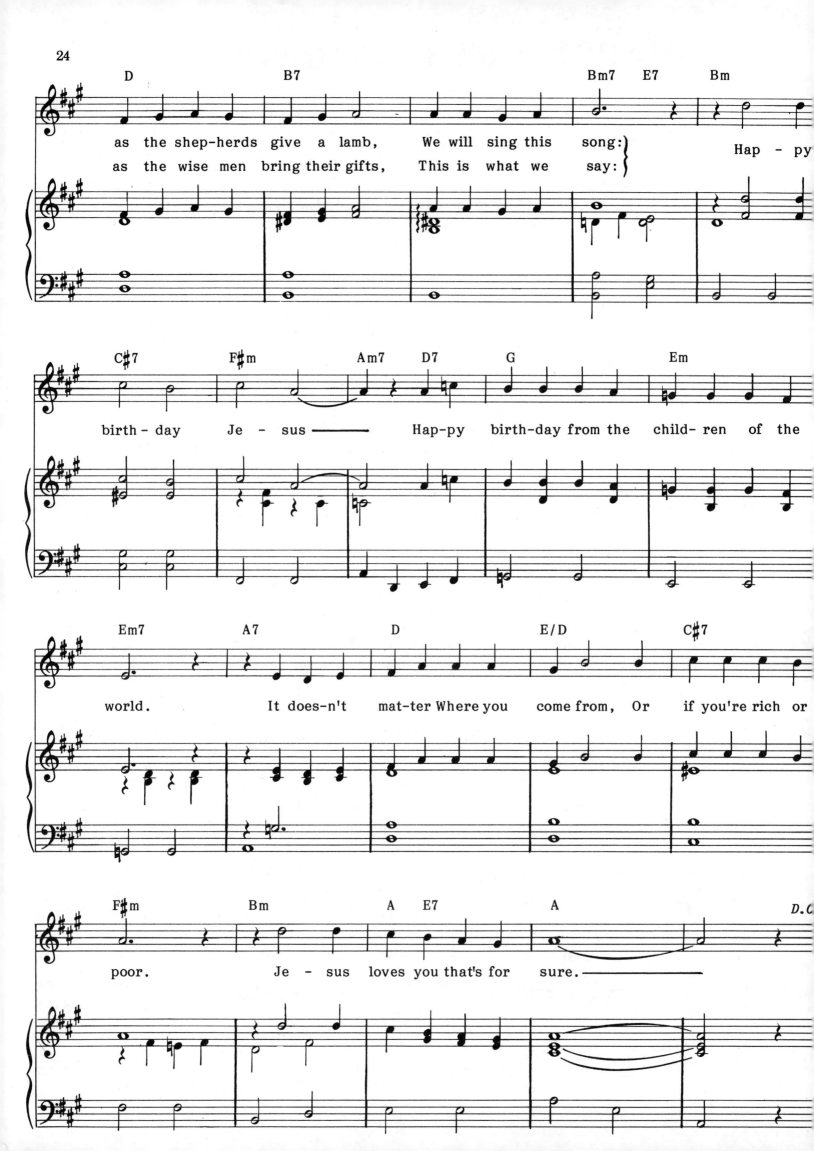